23 AUG 2013

KT-471-257

30131 05069153 1

LONDON BOROUGH OF BARNET

MAXIMUM
RIDE

MAXIMUM RIDE

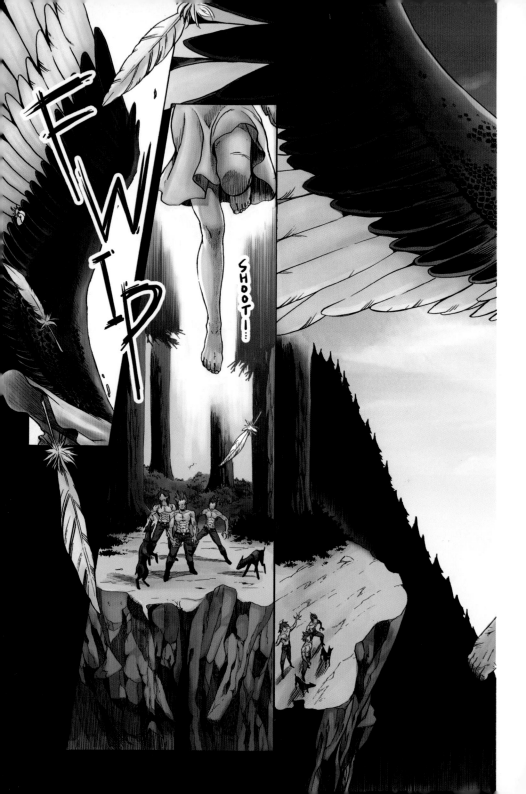

MAXIMUM
RIDE
CHAPTER 1

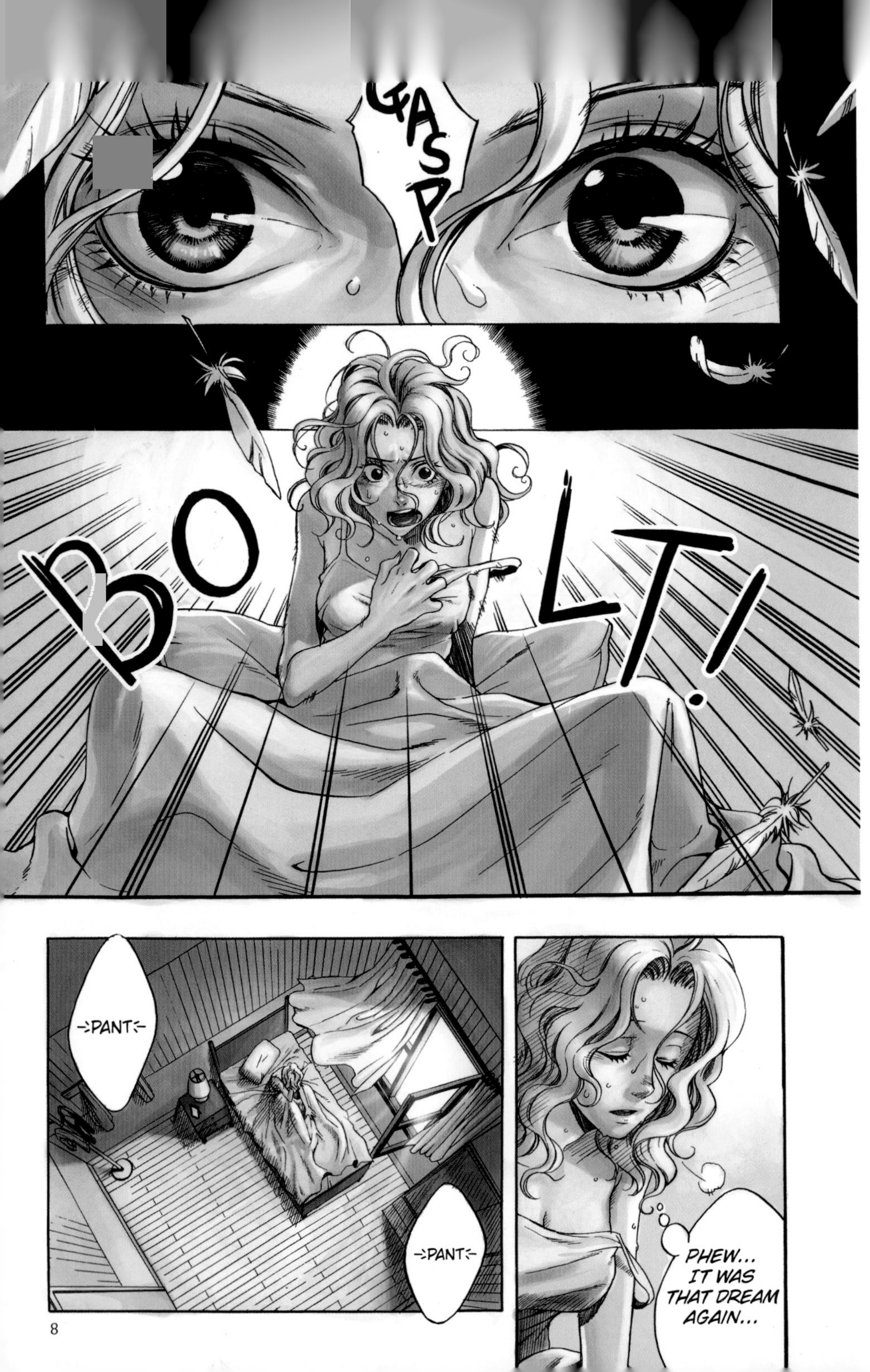
GASP
BOLT!
-PANT-
-PANT-
PHEW... IT WAS THAT DREAM AGAIN...

YAWN~

WHEN WE FIRST MOVED INTO THIS SECLUDED HOUSE...

...JEB BATCHELDER TOOK CARE OF US, LIKE A DAD.

GOOD MORNING, JEB.

TWO YEARS AGO, HE DISAPPEARED. WE ALL KNEW HE WAS DEAD, BUT WE DIDN'T TALK ABOUT IT.

AND NOW, AS THE OLDEST, I'M TRYING TO KEEP THINGS RUNNING IN HIS PLACE...AS BEST I CAN!

WHUMP!!

ACK!

I'LL POUR JUICE.

WOBBLE

WOBBLE

WHO MOVED THE TABLE NEXT TO THE STAIRS?!

SORRY, IGGY.

THE STAIRCASE JUST LOOKED SO EMPTY.

DON'T FORGET I'M BLIND.

THEN PLEASE ACT LIKE YOU ARE.

FLOP

RUMMAGE RUMMAGE

UMM... WISH THE FOOD FAIRIES HAD COME...

MAYBE WE HAVE SOME CANS LEFT.

÷SIGH÷
IT SEEMS LIKE MAKING BREAKFAST IS HARDER THAN MATH.

Not that I'm any good at math.

PRICKLE

SWISH!

SWISH!

HUH?

FWAF!

TWITCH

GAH!

FANG!! WILL YOU QUIT THAT?!

QUIT WHAT? BREATHING?

MAKE SOME NOISE WHEN YOU MOVE! YOU STARTLED ME!

I'LL MAKE EGGS.

WOBBLE

I DON'T WANT MAX TO BURN OUR LAST FRYING PAN.

......

Huh? Fang, when did you get up??

FINE. I'LL GO GET NUDGE AND ANGEL.

......

HI, MAX.

SMILE♥

HEY, YOU'VE ALREADY DRESSED.

CAN YOU DO MY BUTTONS?

16

OKAY, ANGEL, I'LL GO WITH YOU!

TOOT!

?!

I WANT TO GO PICK STRAWBERRIES TODAY.

THEY'RE RIPE NOW.

OH GEEZ, GAZZY!

SMELLY

I'M DONE.

GAS... MASK!

SMELLY

SORRY!

MUNCH MUNCH

YEAH, ANGEL. I THINK THE *FRESH AIR* WOULD DO US ALL GOOD. I'LL GO TOO.

HEH

SMIRK

......

HEH
HEH

WAS THAT YOU?

HOW MANY TIMES HAVE I TOLD YOU NOT TO PLAY JOKES MIMICKING OTHERS?

...KKKH!

HAHAHA

HEH
HEH

ACK! BUT IT'S FUN!

HAHAHA

BETTER NOISES FROM THAT END...

HAHAHA

HA HA

HA...

HA HA...

MAXIMUM
RIDE
CHAPTER 2

YOU WATCH IT!

WHAT HAPPENED?

SSK...

Rummage Rummage

I MEAN, YOU GUYS CAN SEE, CAN'T YOU?

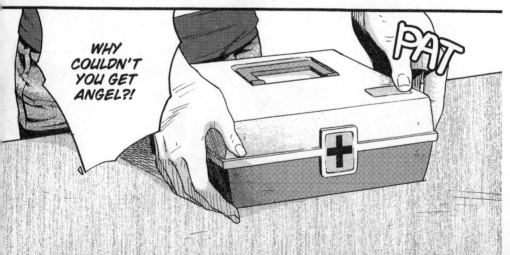

WHY COULDN'T YOU GET ANGEL?!

PAT

......

MAX...

THEY HAD
A CHOPPER!
AND GUNS!
WE'RE NOT
BULLET-
PROOF!!

MAX?

AH...

I'M OKAY...

WHERE'S ANGEL?

ARE YOU UP, MAX?

YEAH...

....

THEY TOOK HER.

SHE'S GONE.

YOU IDIOT!

WHY DIDN'T YOU FOLLOW THEM?!!

ANGEL...

WE HAVE TO FIND HER...

LET'S GO GET HER!!

NOD

NOD

FLAP

FLAP

55

SO...THAT MAKES ME THINK WE HAVE TO GO AFTER ANGEL AGAIN.

BUT THEY WERE IN A CHOPPER. THEY'RE WAY GONE. THEY COULD BE ANYWHERE.

LIKE, CHINA OR SOME-THING...

I DON'T THINK THEY TOOK HER TO CHINA, GAZZY...

WE KNOW EXACTLY WHERE THEY TOOK HER.

WHERE'S THAT?

THE SCHOOL.

THEY TOOK ANGEL BACK TO THE SCHOOL?!

I...THINK SO.

...BUT **WE'D** END UP IN A ZOO.

WELL, WHAT ARE WE GONNA DO, THEN?

FANG, WHERE ARE YOU GOING?

WHAT IS THAT?

EEW. IT STINKS.

SHAKE

SHAKE

NEW NEW AND WINGS AND NEW NEW WINGS GIRL NEW

MUMBLE

......!!

SHAKE SHAKE

MAX... GAZZY...I'M SCARED.

WHAT HAPPENED TO MAX AND THE OTHERS? ARE THEY IN CAGES TOO?

KA

CLANG

OH MY GOD... HARRISON WAS RIGHT.

THEY GOT HER! DO YOU KNOW HOW LONG I'VE WANTED TO GET MY HANDS ON THIS ONE?

DID YOU EVER READ THE DIRECTOR'S PRECEPT REPORT ABOUT THIS RECOMBINANT GROUP?

YEAH, BUT I WASN'T SURE I BELIEVED IT.

ARE YOU SAYING THIS IS SUBJECT ELEVEN? THIS LITTLE GIRL?
SHUDDER!!
COME ON...
OH YES! MAN, WHEN I SECTION HER BRAIN...
CLANK
...LITTLE THING.
SHIVER
SHIVER
YOU'RE WANTED IN LAB SEVEN.

MAXIMUM
RIDE
CHAPTER 3

WHAAAT?

OH...

...YEAH.

GRAB...

WE HAVE TO GO GET ANGEL BACK. WE CAN'T LET HER STAY THERE— WITH THEM.

THEY'RE— MONSTERS. THEY'RE GOING TO DO BAD THINGS TO HER.

AND PUT HER IN A CAGE. HURT HER.

BUT THERE'S FIVE OF US.

SO THE REST OF US HAVE TO GO GET...

Ssk...

......

NOD

HOW FAR...

NUDGE
...

...CALM
DOWN.

...IS IT?

SIX HUNDRED
MILES, MORE
OR LESS.

WHICH
MEANS AT
LEAST...

...A SEVEN-
HOUR FLIGHT,
NOT INCLUDING
BREAKS.

NO USE
DISCUSSING
THIS.

WE'RE WAY
OUTNUMBERED.

YOU ARE SO FULL OF IT.

THAT'S NOT WHY YOU WANT US HERE.

WHY DON'T YOU JUST SAY IT?

......

OKAY.

IT'S TRUE.

I DON'T WANT YOU TO COME.

THE FACT IS, YOU'RE *BLIND*, AND WHILE YOU'RE A GREAT FLYER AROUND HERE WHERE YOU KNOW EVERYTHING...

...I CAN'T BE WORRYING ABOUT YOU IN THE MIDDLE OF A FIGHT WITH THE ERASERS.

WHAT?!!

HOLD ON!

WHAT ABOUT ME?

I DON'T CARE IF THEY HAVE GUNS AND A CHOPPER!

I HAVE TO GO. ANGEL'S MY SISTER!!

THAT'S RIGHT. AND IF THEY WANT HER SO BAD, THEY MIGHT WANT YOU JUST AS BAD.

PLUS, YOU'RE EIGHT YEARS OLD, AND WE'RE GOING TO BE LOGGING MAJOR HOURS.

JEB WOULD NEVER HAVE MADE US STAY.

NEVER EVER!!

MAYBE NOT...

...BUT WE'LL NEVER KNOW.

JEB'S DEAD.

NOW...

...EVERYONE, GET YOUR GEAR TOGETHER.

SO, IN CASE OF EMERGENCY...

...WE ALL CLEAR ON PLAN "B," RIGHT?

UH-HUH!

IF WE GET SEPARATED SOMEHOW—

THOUGH I DON'T SEE HOW WE COULD, UNLESS MAYBE ONE OF US GETS LOST IN A CLOUD...

...OR SOMETHING— DO YOU THINK THAT COULD HAPPEN?

BABBLE

BABBLE BABBLE

I HAVEN'T EVER BEEN INSIDE A CLOUD. I BET IT'S TICKLY.

CAN YOU SEE ANYTHING INSIDE A CLOUD—

WE MEET UP AT THE NORTHMOST POINT OF LAKE MEAD.

RIGHT.

AND WHERE'S THE SCHOOL?

IN DEATH VALLEY, EIGHT MILES DUE NORTH FROM THE BADWATER BASIN.

ANYWAY, I WAS THINKING, NONE OF US EVER KNEW OUR REAL PARENTS, AND, YOU KNOW, WE'VE ALWAYS WONDERED...

...OR AT LEAST I MEAN I'VE ALWAYS WONDERED, BUT I GUESS THE REST OF YOU HAVE TOO, LIKE, WHETHER THEY GAVE US UP VOLUNTARILY OR WHETHER—

NUDGE, I KNOW HOW YOU FEEL.

BUT THOSE NAMES MIGHT NOT HAVE ANYTHING TO DO WITH YOU.

PLEASE, LET'S FOCUS ON RESCUING ANGEL.

......

NUDGE?

YEAH, OKAY.

I WAS JUST THINKING.

......

NUDGE...?

MAX THOUGHT I WOULD GET IN THE WAY, JUST 'COS I'M YOUNG!!

......

-HUFF-

-HUFF-

YOU THINK THE ERASERS WILL COME BACK HERE? LIKE, THEY SAW ALL THE REST OF US. WHY WOULDN'T THEY COME BACK FOR US?

HUH.

'COURSE, IT WOULD BE HARD TO FIND THIS PLACE, AND EVEN HARDER TO GET TO IT.

NOT IF THEY HAVE A CHOPPER!

HUH. THAT'S TRUE.

WE CAN'T JUST SIT HERE AND WAIT FOR THE ERASERS TO GET US!

WE'RE SMART! WE'RE TOUGH AS NAILS! MAX MIGHT NOT HAVE THOUGHT ABOUT KEEPING THE CAMP SAFE, BUT WE DID, AND WE CAN DO IT!

YEAH, I SEE WHAT YOU MEAN.

UHHH... BUT HOW?

SHOOT!!

WE CAN MAKE TRAPS! DO SABOTAGE!

MAKE BOMBS!!

MAX? I'M STARVING!

I COULD EVEN EAT THAT UGLY BIRD!

HANG IN THERE, NUDGE.

Although that really is an ugly bird...

OKAY...

MAX!

IT'S A TOWN.

92

93

TAP

SO, WHAT HAVE YOU GOT TO SAY FOR YOURSELF?

SSK

IS THERE ANY REASON I SHOULDN'T TEACH YOU A LESSON TOO?

WITH MY WINGS FOLDED LIKE THIS...

...I SHOULD LOOK PERFECTLY NORMAL.

SLAM

THUD

RUN!

GET OUT OF HERE!

?!

THIS AIN'T A TOY, YOU IDIOT!

TSK!

GET HER!

THAT STUPID GUN!

I CAN'T FLY IN FRONT OF THEM!!

DUCK

MAXIMUM
RIDE

WHAT HAPPENED, REILLY?!

PANT

PANT

WHAT'S GOING ON HERE?!!

IT BIT REILLY'S HAND AND HE HIT IT!!

DON'T YOU REALIZE HOW UNIQUE THIS "SUBJECT" IS?

THIS IS SUBJECT ELEVEN. DON'T YOU KNOW HOW LONG WE'VE BEEN LOOKING FOR IT? DO NOT DAMAGE THE MERCHANDISE!

I'M NOT A SUBJECT! AND I'M NOT MERCHANDISE EITHER!!

I'M SORRY.

GO TREAT YOUR HAND.

I'LL TAKE OVER HERE.

TAP

OKAY.

FANG? I'M REALLY HUNGRY, YOU KNOW?

WE'LL WAIT HERE FOR MAX. LAKE MEAD IS RIGHT BELOW US.

I'M GONNA DIE OF HUNGER...

OH, FANG, IS THIS CHOCOLATE?!

WHERE DID YOU FIND THIS? HAVE YOU BEEN HIDING IT?!

......

GOD, IT'S SO GOOD.

SO WHERE'S MAX? WHY'D SHE GO DOWN THERE?

SHE SAW SOMEONE IN TROUBLE DOWN BELOW AND WENT TO HELP.

HMMM, THAT DOES SOUND LIKE MAX.

UH...

FANG?

?

THE HUMMER'S COMING.

NEVER KNEW THIS ABANDONED CABIN WOULD HAVE SUCH A PERFECT VIEW OF THE ROAD!!

AND THEY'RE DRIVING WAY TOO FAST.

YEAH, CAN YOU SEE IT THAT WELL?

WHOA, THAT WAS INCREDIBLE!

I HEARD THE EXPLOSION! NOW GIVE ME THE PICTURE!

WE TOTALLY CRUSHED THEM!

WHAT HAPPENED?

ONE FELL OFF THE CLIFF AND GOT SMASHED.

THEN ANY POINT IN DROPPING BIG BOY ON THEM RIGHT NOW?

THE OTHER TWO JUST CRASHED INTO EACH OTHER. THE ERASERS ARE WALKING, SO THEY'RE NOT THAT HURT.

I DON'T THINK SO.

THEY'RE HEADING STRAIGHT INTO THE WOODS. WE'D PROBABLY CAUSE A HUGE FOREST FIRE OR SOMETHING.

THANKS FOR THE RED CARPET.

HOW...HOW DID YOU KNOW WE WERE HERE?

YOU CAN RUN, BUT YOU CAN'T HIDE.

DIDN'T ANYONE EVER TELL YOU?

PEEK

WINDOW'S BLOCKED TOO, IGGY.

UP AND AWAY.

SNIFFLE
SNIFFLE

SSK

...NIGHT,
NUDGE.

SQUEEZE

...NIGHT,
FANG...

168

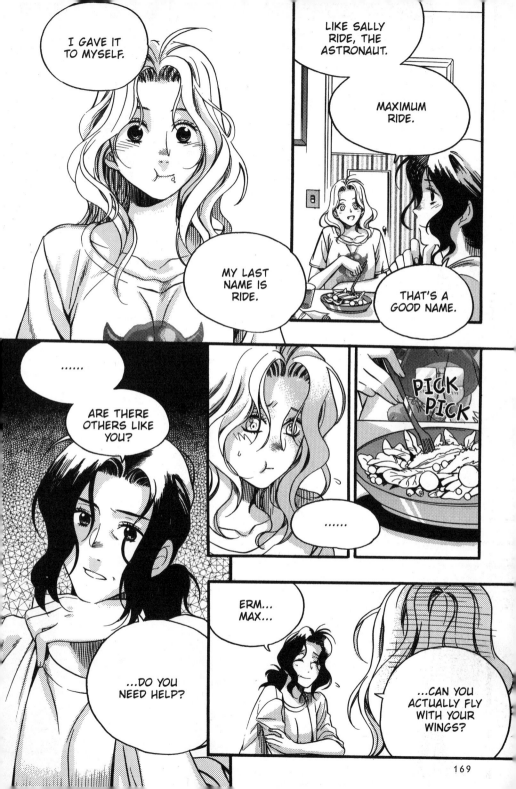

WELL, YEAH.

NOD

MY BONES ARE...THIN.

REALLY? YOU CAN REALLY FLY?

MY BONES ARE THIN AND LIGHT, I HAVE EXTRA MUSCLES, MY LUNGS ARE BIGGER...

...AND MY HEART'S MORE EFFICIENT. BUT I NEED TO EAT A LOT.

IT'S HARD.

AH... I SEE.

173

MAXIMUM
RIDE

UM... THANKS FOR THE MEAL.

I...

...SHOULD LEAVE NOW.

YEAH, SOME FRIENDS ARE WAITING FOR ME.

IT'S REALLY IMPORTANT.

ALREADY?

HOW WILL YOU GET TO THEM?

CAN I GIVE YOU A RIDE?

NO...

I NEED TO, UM, FLY THERE. BUT I DON'T THINK I CAN YET.

IT WOULD BE DANGEROUS FOR YOU TO STRAIN YOUR INJURY BEFORE IT'S HEALED.

AS OF NOW, I CAN'T TELL YOU THE FULL EXTENT OF IT.

BUT I COULD GIVE YOU A BETTER IDEA IF WE HAD AN X-RAY.

A-HA-HA-HA-HA-HA! NO, NOT ALL OF US HAVE SUPER-HUMAN POWERS, YOU KNOW.

DO YOU HAVE X-RAY VISION?

BUT SOME OF US HAVE ACCESS TO X-RAY MACHINES.

GRIN

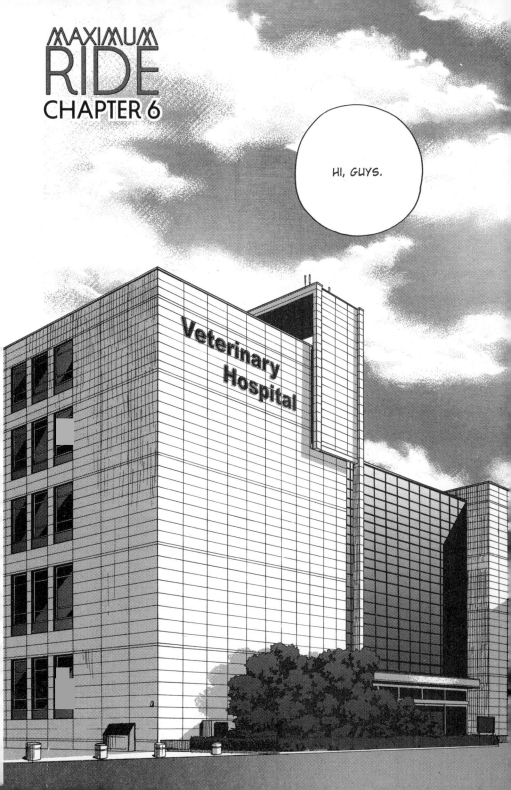

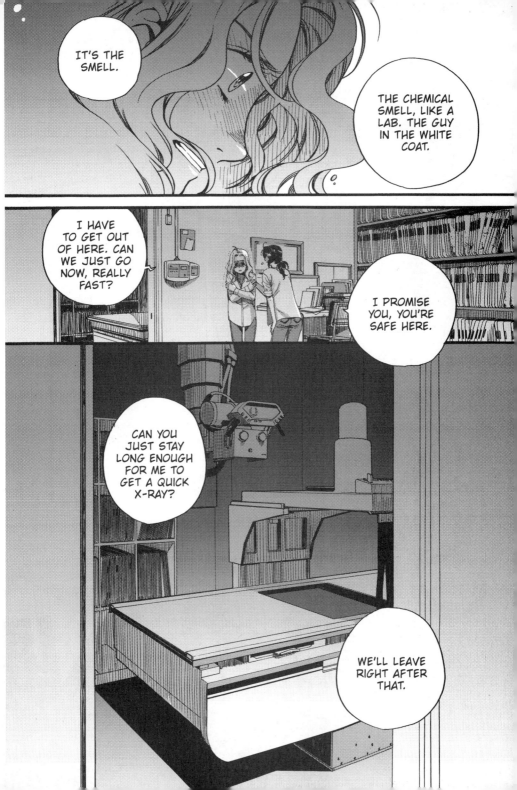

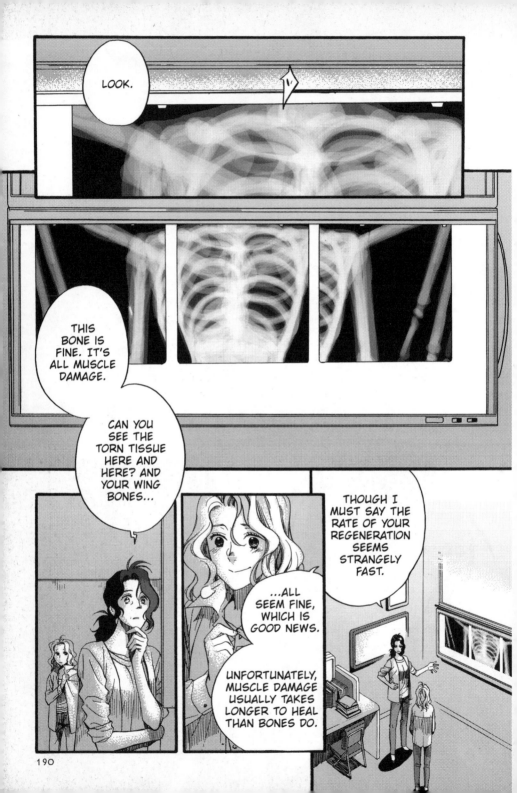

LOOK.

THIS BONE IS FINE. IT'S ALL MUSCLE DAMAGE.

CAN YOU SEE THE TORN TISSUE HERE AND HERE? AND YOUR WING BONES...

THOUGH I MUST SAY THE RATE OF YOUR REGENERATION SEEMS STRANGELY FAST.

...ALL SEEM FINE, WHICH IS GOOD NEWS.

UNFORTUNATELY, MUSCLE DAMAGE USUALLY TAKES LONGER TO HEAL THAN BONES DO.

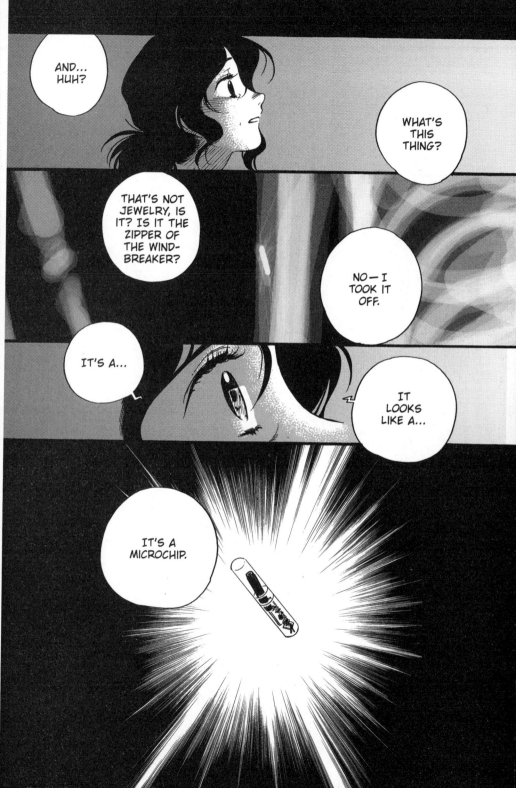

WE PUT SOMETHING SIMILAR ON ANIMALS TO IDENTIFY THEM IN CASE THEY GET LOST. YOURS LOOKS LIKE A...

...LIKE THE ONES WE USE ON REALLY EXPENSIVE PETS, SHOW DOGS AND SUCH. THEY HAVE A TRACER IN THEM IN CASE THEY GET STOLEN. THEY CAN BE TRACKED, WHEREVER THEY GO.

I'M NOT SAYING THAT'S WHAT IT IS...

THAT'S JUST WHAT IT LOOKS LIKE.

TAKE IT OUT! PLEASE TAKE IT OUT RIGHT NOW.

SHAKE SHAKE

I DON'T THINK IT CAN BE SURGICALLY REMOVED.

I'M SORRY, MAX.

WHAT'S GOING ON HERE?

SORRY, MA'AM.

DOCTOR!

SORRY, DOCTOR.

FORGIVE US FOR INTERRUPTING. THERE'S NOTHING TO WORRY ABOUT. WE'RE WITH THE LOCAL AUTHORITIES.

WE'RE LOOKING FOR ANYTHING UNUSUAL...

UNUSUAL LIKE WHAT? SUGAR-FREE SODA THAT ACTUALLY TASTES GOOD?

NO. UNUSUAL PEOPLE, FOR INSTANCE. A STRANGER IN THE NEIGH-BORHOOD.

CHILDREN OR TEENAGERS YOU DON'T KNOW OR WHO LOOK SUSPICIOUS. OR UNUSUAL ANIMALS, EVEN.

I'M A VETERINARY SURGEON. I USUALLY DON'T LOOK AT MY PATIENTS' OWNERS MUCH, AND I HAVEN'T SEEN ANY STRANGERS AROUND.

AS FAR AS UNUSUAL ANIMALS, LAST WEEK I TREATED A COW THAT HAD A BICORNUATE UTERUS. SHE HAD A HEALTHY CALF ON EACH SIDE.

FANG...

...YOU REALLY THINK EVERYONE'S DEAD?

HERE WE GO! FRESH-BAKED CHOCOLATE-CHIP COOKIES!

WOW!

THEY SMELL SO GOOD! ♡

HOOOOT

HAHAHA

YOU'D THINK YOU'D NEVER TASTED HOME-MADE COOKIES BEFORE.

HAVEN'T.

REALLY?

NO...THIS TASTES LIKE HEAVEN.

......

TAKE THESE WITH YOU ON YOUR WAY HOME.

THANK YOU.

W-WAIT! WHAT'S GOING ON?!

......

...PROBABLY NOT...

MAX, TAKE THIS BAG.

N-NO, IT'S OKAY.

PLEASE TAKE IT. IT'S AN OLD ONE— I DON'T USE IT ANYMORE. AND...I PUT MY PHONE NUMBER INSIDE.

IF YOU EVER NEED ANYTHING, ANYTHING AT ALL, PLEASE CALL US. I ALSO PUT SOME MONEY IN, JUST IN CASE.

AH... BUT...

IT'S NOT MUCH, SO PLEASE TAKE IT WITH YOU. I JUST... FEEL LIKE YOU'RE A DAUGHTER TO ME.

......

THANK YOU...

...THEY ACCEPTED ME FOR WHO I AM. IF THEY WERE MY FAMILY...

MAXIMUM RIDE
CHAPTER 7

FANG... NUDGE...

DID THEY EVER MAKE IT HERE? WHAT IF —

MAX!

NUDGE!

MAX! MAX! I CAN'T BELIEVE IT! **CAN** I BELIEVE IT?

LET'S GO BACK TO THE CAVE AND TALK.

NO...

WAS IT... WAS IT AFTER THE OIL-SLICK HUMMER CRASH?

OIL-SLICK HUMMER CRASH?!

YOU GUYS SET OFF A BOMB? DIDN'T THAT TELL THE ERASERS EXACTLY WHERE YOU WERE?

YOU SHOULD HAVE STAYED HIDDEN!

BUT THEY ALREADY KNEW WHERE WE WERE!

THEY'D SEEN ALL OF US— THEY KNEW WE WERE IN THE AREA.

OR MAYBE IT WAS... AFTER THE BOMB.

I THINK IT WAS THE BOMB. THAT DEFINITELY SEEMED TO TICK THEM OFF.

BOMB?!

......!!

THERE'S A MICROCHIP IN YOUR FORE-ARM.

WELL, I'M GLAD YOU'RE SAFE.

HOW WERE YOU GUYS, FANG AND NUDGE?

SORRY TO KEEP YOU WAITING...

I...TRIED TO FIND MY MOM FROM THE ADDRESS I SAW IN THE FILES.

WHAAAT? YOUR MOM?

BUT THE ERASERS, INCLUDING THAT DIRTBAG ARI, SHOWED UP AND GAVE FANG A HARD TIME.

SO YOU DIDN'T TALK TO HER? DID SHE LOOK NICE?

...UM...

...I'LL TELL YOU ABOUT IT LATER.

SHRUG

AH...

Went that bad, huh?

WE'VE LEARNED SOME STUFF FROM THE HAWKS.

SOME BANKING MOVES, HOW THEY COMMUNICATE, STUFF LIKE THAT.

HAWKS ARE REALLY COOL.

CAN YOU TEACH US WHAT YOU LEARNED?

RIGHT! THEY, LIKE, USE THE TIPS OF THEIR FEATHERS TO HELP THEM AIM, AND WE TRIED IT, AND IT WAS AMAZING. A LITTLE THING LIKE THAT MAKES SUCH A DIFFERENCE.

YEAH, SURE.

NOD

AND I DON'T KNOW IF ANY OF YOU HAVE ONE...

...THERE MIGHT NOT BE ANY "SAFE ZONE" FOR US.

BUT WE CAN'T TURN BACK NOW.

NO MATTER WHAT...

...WE'RE GOING AFTER ANGEL.

MAX, I'M STARVING.

WE HAVEN'T EATEN ANYTHING SINCE THOSE CHOCOLATE-CHIP COOKIES...

IT WOULD BE NICE TO TAKE OUR TIME, BUT WE DON'T KNOW WHEN THE ERASERS WILL SHOW UP.

LET'S HURRY AND FINISH OUR MEAL SO WE CAN LEAVE RIGHT AWAY.

ESPECIALLY IF THERE REALLY IS A MICROCHIP IN MY ARM.

OKAY!

......

ELLA...

DR. MARTINEZ...

BOLT

FANG... NOD

PEEK...

NUDGE

DON'T LOOK UP. IN THREE SECONDS ...

...JUMP OVER FANG AND OUT THAT EXIT DOOR.

SLURP

TAP

231

BOLT

DAMN IT, THEY'RE OUT HERE TOO! LOOK OUT!

MAXIMUM RIDE.

OH, I'VE MISSED YOU SO MUCH.

JEB
BATCHELDER?!

♡ Afterword from NaRae Lee ♡

MY AFTERWORD FOR CHAPTER SEVEN AND THE COLLECTED BOOK!

WOW~ I CAN'T BELIEVE THE FIRST VOLUME OF THE BOOK IS ALREADY DONE!!

Hair already growing out (messy)

WHEN MY EDITOR FIRST ASKED ME TO WORK ON MAXIMUM RIDE, I DIDN'T KNOW IT WAS THIS HUGE A PROJECT. T.T I DIDN'T REALLY HAVE MUCH TIME TO THINK, BUT I THOUGHT IT WAS A GREAT OPPORTUNITY AND STARTED ON IT...I NEVER THOUGHT I WOULD BE PUBLISHED FAR AWAY IN AMERICA! (ESPECIALLY ON A BESTSELLER TITLE!!)

SO IT'S SIMPLE. YOU JUST HAVE TO DRAW FOR AN AMERICAN MAGAZINE.

?？?!

HUH?! AMERICA?!

ONLY AFTER I MET THE DIRECTOR DID I ACTUALLY REALIZE THAT I WAS WORKING WITH AN AMERICAN PUBLISHER. BEFORE THAT, SINCE IT WAS SO OUT OF THE BLUE, I THOUGHT MY EDITOR MIGHT JUST BE JOKING WITH ME. (LOL)

ABCDEFG

The director who I now can't remember that clearly. T.T

GAH~! HE'S A REAL FOREIGNER!

AND THEN BEFORE I REALIZED IT, THE SERIALIZATION HAD STARTED AND I WAS WORKING ON MAXIMUM RIDE.

I TOLD THE DIRECTOR THAT I WOULD PRACTICE MY ENGLISH BEFORE I MET HIM AGAIN...

Too hard!

...BUT I HAVE BEEN SO BUSY THAT NOT ONLY DID I NOT LEARN ENGLISH, BUT I ALSO FORGOT THE JAPANESE I HAD LEARNED... T.T

BUT I STILL REMEMBER HIM SAYING, "YOU'RE MORE ATTRACTIVE 'COS YOU DON'T SPEAK ENGLISH. MORE EXOTIC." (I'M ATTRACTIVE!!)

<< THE DESK I WORK ON. THIS IS MY ROOM AT MY PARENTS' HOUSE. I USE THE COMPUTER TO DO THE TONING OR TO WORK ON PROJECTS OTHER THAN MAXIMUM RIDE.

I USED TO PENCIL A LOT AT A NEARBY CAFÉ. IT CAN GET A LITTLE STUFFY IF YOU STAY HOME FOR TOO LONG...

ESPECIALLY IN THE SUMMER, I WENT TO ENJOY THE COOL ICED COFFEE AND THE AIR CONDITIONING!!

Go work at your own house!

AND FOR THE INKING, I MOSTLY WORK AT MY BACKGROUND ASSISTANT FRIEND'S HOUSE. WE GO TO THE SAME SCHOOL NOW AND ALSO WENT TO THE SAME HIGH SCHOOL, SO IT'S COMFY AND NICE. (IS IT JUST COMFY FOR ME?!)

BY THE TIME I START ON THE SECOND VOLUME I WILL HAVE MY OWN STUDIO!

COME HOME!! ← Mom.

EVERY TIME THE DEADLINE GOT CLOSE, SOMETHING WOULD BREAK... (THE MONITOR, THE KEYBOARD, AND MY CELL PHONE WAS EVEN OUT OF ORDER TILL NOW... RECENTLY, MY HARD DRIVE SEEMS TO BE ILL TOO, SO I'M WORRIED...)

...OR THIS AND THAT WOULD HAPPEN TO ME PERSONALLY (EVERY TIME, EITHER ME OR MY ASSISTANT WOULD GET SICK) MAKING IT HARDER TO MEET THE DEADLINE.

COUGH COUGH

BUT I'M HAPPY I STILL MANAGED TO COME THIS FAR, TO HAVE THIS HEAVY NUMBER OF PAGES.

IT'S ALL THANKS TO MY EDITOR'S KIND SUPPORT AND PRAISE.

THEY SAY COMPLIMENTS WILL MAKE EVEN A WHALE DANCE! THANK YOU SO MUCH, MY EDITOR! VISIT KOREA SOON. ^^

total 240p ?

IN ADDITION TO MAXIMUM RIDE, I STARTED A NEW SERIES IN KOREA AS WELL. IT IS A TITLE FOR LITTLE GIRLS CALLED SWEETIE MILKY PROPOSAL. (I THINK AMERICANS MIGHT LAUGH AT THE TITLE... T.T;;)

IT'S VERY DIFFERENT FROM MAXIMUM RIDE.

IT'S EIGHT PAGES A MONTH... I HOPE IT GOES WELL AND SOMEDAY I WILL GET TO SHOW IT TO THE AMERICAN READERS TOO. ^^

ANYWAY, IT'S ALREADY
BEEN TEN MONTHS SINCE I STARTED
WORKING ON MAXIMUM RIDE!! I REALLY FELL
IN LOVE WITH THE SIX MAIN CHARACTERS!
(SOMETIMES I FEEL LIKE THEY'RE MY OWN
LITTLE BROTHERS AND SISTERS.)

SOMETIMES WHEN I'M WORKING
HARD, MAX AND THE FLOCK APPEAR IN MY
DREAMS AND WE ALL FLY TOGETHER! (LOL)

NO TIME TO
SLEEP! LET'S GO
WORK!!!

NoNooo

Argh...
Don't do
this...

Why is Max
speaking in Korean
anyway??

HONESTLY...I STILL CAN'T BELIEVE
THE FACT THAT THE MAXIMUM RIDE I DREW
IS SELLING IN A LAND MUCH LARGER THAN
KOREA. (IT DOESN'T HELP THAT I NEVER GOT
TO ACTUALLY SEE IT IN STORES. T.T)
IT STILL FEELS LIKE A DREAM!!

It's even
in stores
here!!

I WANT TO SEE MY
BOOK IN BOOKSTORES
TOO. SOB-SOB...

Friend who lives
in Canada

I KNOW I HAVE A
LOT TO LEARN, BUT I
HOPE YOU KEEP ENJOYING
MAXIMUM RIDE!!

IF YOU CAN READ KOREAN
OR YOU WANT TO SEE MORE OF MY ART,
PLEASE COME AND VISIT MY BLOG!
HTTP://BLOG.NAVER.COM/NARE870815

I WANT TO SEND MY SPECIAL THANKS TO
JUYOUN LEE, MY EDITOR, MOONJU, WHO HELPED
ME WITH THE BACKGROUNDS, DONGWOO, WHO
HELPED ME WITH ERASING AND THE INKS, MY
MOTHER, WHO ALWAYS WORRIES ABOUT MY
HEALTH, AND LASTLY ALL THE PROFESSORS AT
CHUNGKANG UNIVERSITY.

THANK YOU SO, SO MUCH!!

MAXIMUM RIDE: THE MANGA ①

JAMES PATTERSON
& NaRae Lee

Adaptation and Illustration: NaRae Lee

Lettering: Abigail Blackman

Published in the United Kingdom by Arrow Books in 2009

5 7 9 10 8 6

Copyright © SueJack, Inc. 2009

Illustrations © Hachette Book Group, Inc. 2009

James Patterson and NaRae Lee have asserted their right under the Copyright, Designs and Patents Act, 1988 to be identified as the authors of this work.

This novel is a work of fiction. Names and characters are the product of the author's imagination and any resemblance to actual persons, living or dead, is entirely coincidental

This book is sold subject to the condition that it shall not, by way of trade or otherwise, be lent, resold, hired out, or otherwise circulated without the publisher's prior consent in any form of binding or cover other than that in which it is published and without a similar condition, including this condition, being imposed on the subsequent purchaser

First published in Great Britain in 2009 by Arrow

Arrow Books
Random House, 20 Vauxhall Bridge Road,
London SW1V 2SA

www.rbooks.co.uk

Addresses for companies within The Random House Group Limited can be found at:
www.randomhouse.co.uk/offices.htm

The Random House Group Limited Reg. No. 954009

A CIP catalogue record for this book
is available from the British Library

ISBN 9780099538363

The Random House Group Limited supports the Forest Stewardship Council® (FSC®), the leading international forest-certification organisation. Our books carrying the FSC label are printed on FSC®-certified paper. FSC is the only forest-certification scheme supported by the leading environmental organisations, including Greenpeace. Our paper procurement policy can be found at: www.randomhouse.co.uk/environment

MIX
Paper from
responsible sources
FSC® C014496

Printed and bound in Germany by GGP Media GmbH, Pößneck

NOW AVAILABLE IN PAPERBACK

MAX
A MAXIMUM RIDE NOVEL

James Patterson

Nobody said saving the world be easy.

Until now, Max and the flock have lived a lonely existence: hunted down, tortured, and pushed to the fringe of society. Always on the run, they have never been able to live a normal life. But things are changing.

The flock have finally found acceptance for their extraordinary skills. They don't have to hide away and longer – far from it: now everyone wants to see just what they can do. But fame and fortune always come at a price and Max isn't ready for all the glitz and glamour just yet. Meanwhile, sinister forces are plotting their attack, putting more than just the flock in danger.

Something deadly is lurking in the depths of the ocean. As the flock uncover a terrible secret set to threaten the world, can they save the day? Or is this a disaster too tough to tackle, even for them?

arrow books

For a sneak preview of **MAX** read on . . .

1

There.

Devin raised his right arm and focused his sight directly over his wrist. It took less than a millisecond to calculate the trajectory—he didn't have a built-in computer, but his IQ of 220 served him well.

He breathed in and out slowly, getting ready to squeeze the trigger in between breaths, in between heartbeats. His sensitive nose almost wrinkled as the ever-present smog that hovered over the Los Angeles basin filled his lungs. He hated to think what the pollutants were doing to his brain cells, but some things were necessary evils.

There.

His light eyes perfectly tracked the objects flying overhead: one, two, three, four, five, six. Seven? There was a small seventh object, unexpected, but quickly determined to be unimportant. Actually, all of them were unimportant. All but one. The one in front.

He knew they had raptor vision. He himself had merely extraordinary eyesight. It was good enough. All the same, the gunsight attached to his wrist provided him with crosshairs that made missing an impossibility. He never missed.

That's why they saved him for extra-special missions like this one.

Many, many others had already failed at this task. Devin felt utter disdain for them. To kill one birdkid—how hard could it be? They were flesh and blood—ridiculously fragile. It wasn't like bullets bounced off them.

Once more Devin raised his arm and sighted his prey, catching her neatly in the crosshairs, as if they could pin her to the sky. The flock flew in a large arc overhead, perfectly spaced, the one called Maximum in front, flanked by the two large males. Then a smaller female. Then a smaller male and the smallest female, in a row after him.

Finally, a smallish black object, not birdkid shaped, struggled to keep up. Devin couldn't identify it—it hadn't been in his dossier. The closest thing he could imagine was if someone grafted wings onto a small dog or something, as unlikely as that was.

But Max was the only one he was concerned with. It was Max he was supposed to kill, Max whom he kept catching in his sights.

Devin sighed and lowered his arm. This was almost too easy. It wasn't sporting. He loved the chase, the hunt, the split-second intersection of luck and aim that allowed him to exercise his perfection, his inability to miss.

He looked down at where his right hand had been. One could get used to having no right hand. It was surprisingly easy. And it was so superior to have this lovely weapon instead.

It wasn't as crude as simply having a Glock 18 grafted to his amputated limb. It was so much more elegant than that, so much more a miracle of design and ingenuity. This weapon was physically a part of him, responsive to his slightest thought, triggered by almost imperceptible nerve firings taking place in the interface between his arm and the weapon.

He was a living work of art.

Unlike the birdkids, flying in traceable patterns overhead. Devin had seen the posters, the advertisements. Those naïve, do-gooder idiots at the Coalition to Stop the Madness had organized this whole thing, this air show, this demonstration of supposedly "evolved" humans.

Wrong. The birdkids were ill-conceived accidents. He, Devin, was truly an evolved human.

The CSM zealots were wasting their time—and everyone else's. Using the birdkids to promote their own agenda was a typically selfish, shortsighted thing to do—manipulating and taking advantage of lesser creatures in order to "save" even lesser creatures. It was a joke.

A joke that could not be perpetrated without this flock of examples. And the flock could not exist without its leader.

Once again Devin raised his arm and closed his left eye to focus through the sight attached to his wrist. He angled the Glock a millimeter to the left, and smoothly tracked his target as she arced across the sky.

One breath in, one breath out. One heartbeat, two heartbeats, and here we go . . .

James
Patterson

To find out more about James Patterson
and his bestselling books, go to
www.jamespatterson.co.uk